Harry Potter™

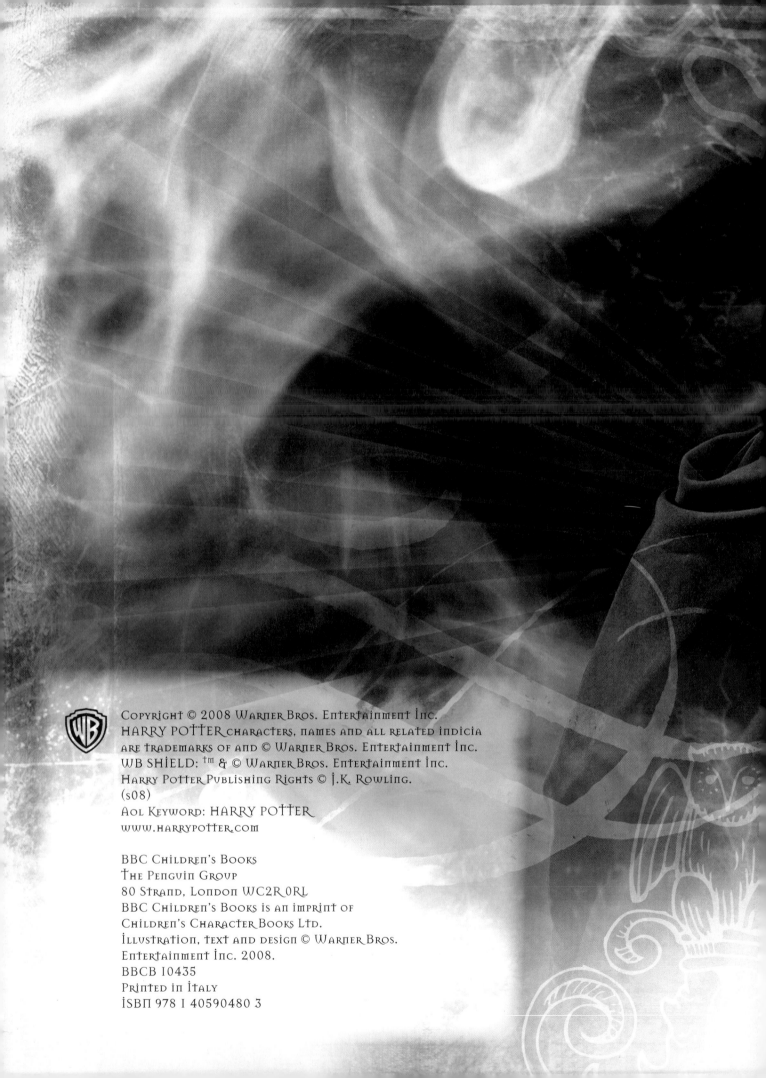

BBC Children's Books
The Penguin Group
80 Strand, London WC2R 0RL
BBC Children's Books is an imprint of
Children's Character Books Ltd.
Illustration, text and design © Warner Bros.
Entertainment Inc. 2008.
BBCB 10435
Printed in Italy
ISBN 978 1 40590480 3

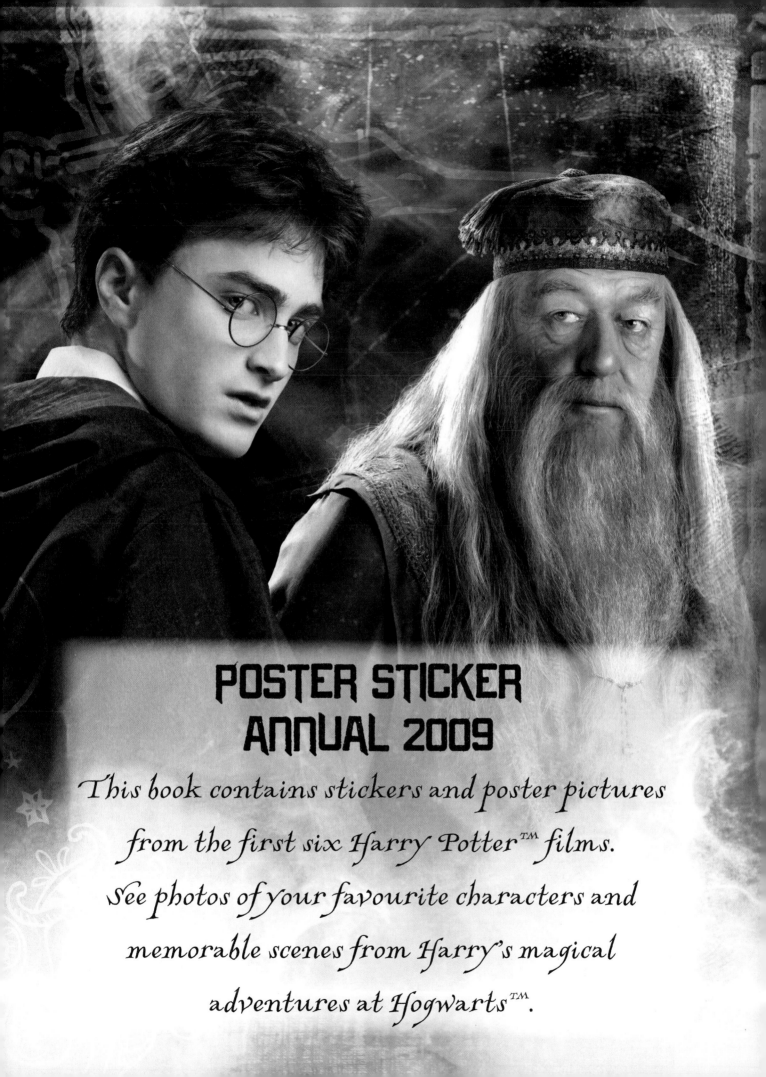

POSTER STICKER ANNUAL 2009

This book contains stickers and poster pictures from the first six Harry Potter™ films. See photos of your favourite characters and memorable scenes from Harry's magical adventures at Hogwarts™.

HOGWARTS
SCHOOL OF
WITCHCRAFT AND
WIZARDRY™

The Black Lake

Hogwarts Express™

HOGWARTS EXPRESS 5972

9¾

HOGWARTS EXPRESS

No. 257

The Great Hall

The Sorting Hat™

the Forbidden Forest

HOGWARTS™
HOUSES

Gryffindor™

HEAD OF HOUSE: Professor Minerva McGonagall

FOUNDER: Godric Gryffindor

GHOST: Nearly Headless Nick™

Ravenclaw™

HEAD OF HOUSE: Professor Filius Flitwick

FOUNDER: Rowena Ravenclaw

GHOST: The Grey Lady™

Hufflepuff™

HEAD OF HOUSE: Professor Pomona Sprout

FOUNDER: Helga Hufflepuff

GHOST: The Fat Friar

Slytherin™

HEAD OF HOUSE: Professor Severus Snape

FOUNDER: Salazar Slytherin

GHOST: The Bloody Baron™

STAFF
ALBUS
DUMBLEDORE™

*H*eadmaster of Hogwarts

Friend and mentor to Harry

SEVERUS SNAPE™

Potions teacher during Harry's first five years at Hogwarts, Severus Snape is finally named Defence against the Dark Arts professor during Harry's sixth year - and is eventually revealed to be the Half-Blood Prince.

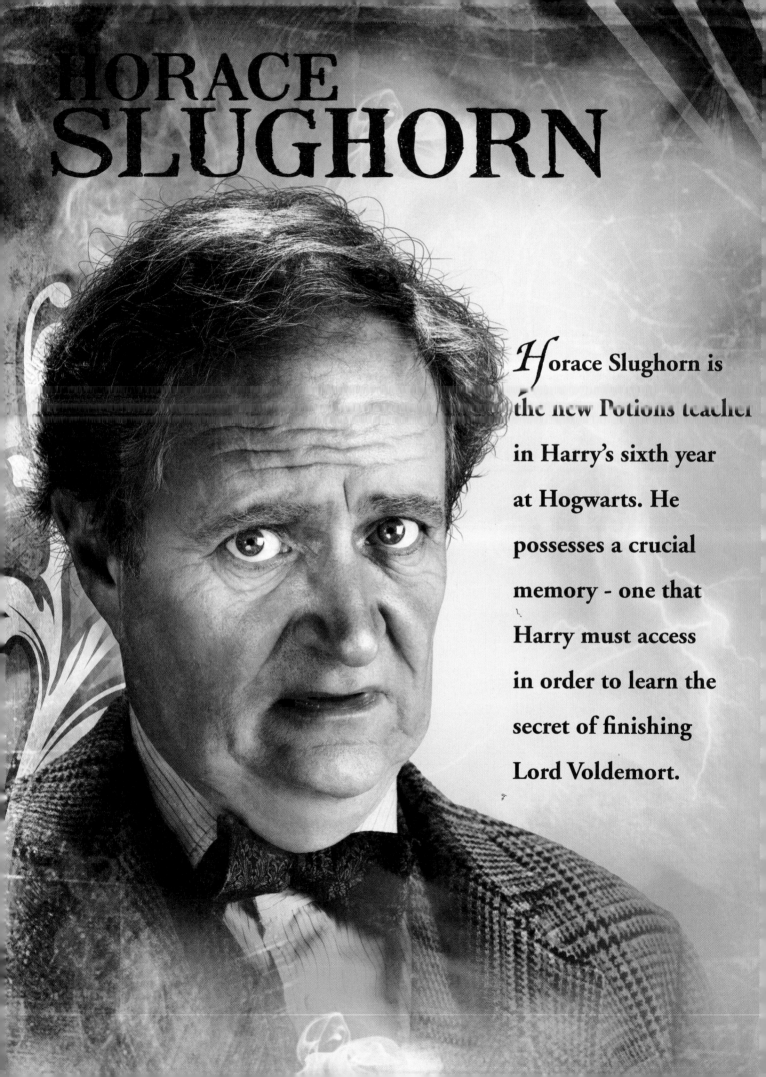

HORACE SLUGHORN

*H*orace Slughorn is the new Potions teacher in Harry's sixth year at Hogwarts. He possesses a crucial memory - one that Harry must access in order to learn the secret of finishing Lord Voldemort.

EXTREMELY POISONOUS

POTION N.86

CONTAINS: POWDERED MOONSTONE & SYRUP OF HELLEBORE

№ 65487

EXTR
POISO

OTT
N.0

№ 66548

Minerva McGonagall™

Deputy Headmistress, Transfiguration teacher, Head of Gryffindor house

Pomona Sprout

Herbology teacher and Head of Hufflepuff house

Filius Flitwick

Charms teacher and Head of Ravenclaw house

Rubeus Hagrid™

**Keeper of Keys and Grounds
and Care of Magical
Creatures teacher**

Sybill Trelawney

Divination teacher

DEFENCE AGAINST THE DARK ARTS

Quirinus Quirrell

Year One

Gilderoy Lockhart™

Year Two

Remus Lupin

Year Three

Alastor 'Mad-Eye' Moody

Year Four

Dolores Umbridge™

Year Five

Severus Snape™

Year Six

POTIONS

*P*otions is one of the subjects taught at Hogwarts.

*H*orace Slughorn teaches students about Felix Felicis during Harry's sixth year.

*H*ermione brews
Polyjuice Potion.

*R*on accidentally
takes love potion
meant for Harry.

SPELLS
AND CHARMS

*H*arry conjures his Patronus, a stag.

*D*umbledore battles Voldemort at the Ministry of Magic.

*H*ermione casts *Immobilus* at Cornish pixies in Lockhart's Defence Against the Dark Arts class.

*S*nape tries to teach Harry the art of Occlumency - the magical defence of the mind against external penetration.

LOVE AND FRIENDSHIP

Harry Potter™

Harry develops feelings for Ginny during his sixth year at Hogwarts.

Cho Chang

Cho and Harry develop a romantic relationship during their fifth year at Hogwarts.

Ginny Weasley™

Ginny has had a crush on Harry since she first met him.

Cedric Diggory

Cedric and Cho attended the Yule Ball together during their fourth year.

Lavender Brown

Lavender and Ron spend much of their sixth year snogging.

Ron Weasley™

Ron is unable to acknowledge his feelings for Hermione.

Viktor Krum

Viktor was Hermione's date at the Yule Ball.

Hermione Granger™

Hermione is not happy about Ron's relationship with Lavender during their sixth year.

TM & © WBEI (s08)

TM & © WBEI (s08)

TM & © WBEI (s08)

The Weasleys

Arthur and Molly Weasley have seven children:
Bill, Charlie, Percy, Fred, George, Ron and Ginny.

ANTI-VOLDEMORT MOVEMENT

Luna Lovegood™

Luna joined Harry in battle at the Ministry of Magic during their fifth year.

Neville Longbottom™

A loyal friend to Harry, Neville also lost his parents to Voldemort when Death Eater Bellatrix Lestrange tortured them into madness.

*H*arry and his friends formed Dumbledore's Army during their fifth year to practise defensive magic.

ROOM OF REQUIREMENT

Draco Malfoy uses the Room of Requirement during his sixth year to let the Death Eaters into Hogwarts.

The D.A. practice defensive magic in the Room of Requirement during Harry's fifth year.

ORDER OF THE PHOENIX™

Number 12 Grimmauld Place is Headquarters to the Order of the Phoenix… and Sirius Black's family home.

Sirius Black ™

Harry's godfather and an Animagus

Albus Dumbledore™

Founder and Head of the Order of the Phoenix

Nymphdora Tonks™

An Auror and a Metamorphmagus, Tonks
can change her appearance at will.

Remus Lupin

Because he is a werewolf, Lupin is reluctant to form a romantic relationship with Tonks.

Alastor 'Mad-eye' Moody

Ex-Auror Mad-Eye has a spinning glass eye that seems to be able to see in every direction.

MINISTRY OF MAGIC

The Ministry of Magic governs the magical community.

Dolores Umbridge™

Hogwarts' High Inquisitor during Harry's fifth year

Cornelius Fudge

Minister for Magic until Harry's sixth year

Ministry Proclamations

The Ministry of Magic passes laws for the wizarding world.

PROCLAMATION.

EDUCATIONAL DECREE

☞ No.

THOSE WISHING TO JOIN THE INQUISITIONAL SQUAD

for EXTRA CREDIT
May sign up in the
High Inquisitor's
OFFICE

✠

As Referred to
in Decree No. 157 of 1924,
formerly known to be the Ministerial
Management of Magical Mayhem Act No. 792/B
& subject to Approval by The Very Important Members of Section M.17rs
Blah blahblah al Abbiah bla-H / Blahbl ah Niahia Blu Abbiah bla-H Abbiah blahblah Bla blaX blahblah D

Barty Crouch

**Previously Head
of the Department
of International
Magical Co-operation**

QUIDDITCH™

*H*arry is Seeker and Captain of Gryffindor's Quidditch team in his sixth year at Hogwarts.

Ron is Keeper for
Gryffindor's Quidditch
team in his sixth year
at Hogwarts.

MAGICAL CREATURES

Merpeople

They live in the lake at Hogwarts.

Buckbeak™

A Hippogriff

Fawkes™

A Phoenix

Grawp

Hagrid's giant half-brother

Dobby™

A house-elf

The Hungarian Horntail Dragon

Battled by Harry during the Triwizard Tournament

Werewolf

Remus Lupin, transformed

Basilisk

The monster in the Chamber of Secrets during Harry's second year

Mountain Troll

Battled by Harry and Ron during their first year

DEATH EATERS

Lucius Malfoy

Death Eater - and father to Draco Malfoy

Barty Crouch Junior

A Death Eater who casts the Dark Mark at the Quidditch World Cup

Bellatrix Lestrange

The Death Eater who killed Sirius Black and tortured Neville Longbottom's parents

Draco Malfoy™

Draco joins the Death Eaters during his sixth year at Hogwarts.

Death Eater Mask

Death Eaters wear frightening masks to hide their real identities.

UNFORGIVEABLE CURSES

Avada Kedavra

The Killing Curse: causes
instant, unexplainable death.

Mad-Eye
Moody teaches
Harry and his
friends about the
Unforgiveable Curses.

Crucio

The Cruciatus Curse: inflicts unbearable pain on the victim.

Imperio

The Imperius Curse: allows the caster to control the victim.

THE DARKLORD

Tom Riddle™

Dumbledore visits the young Voldemort, Tom Riddle, in the orphange.

Riddle's diary

Tom Riddle disappears when Harry destroys his diary in the Chamber of Secrets during his second year at Hogwarts.

Lord Voldemort™

'He-Who-Must-Not-Be-Named' was born Tom Marvolo Riddle.

Nagini

Voldemort's snake

HORCRUXES

Dumbledore and Harry suspect that Voldemort divided his soul into six Horcruxes: Tom Riddle's diary, Marvolo Gaunt's ring, Slytherin's locket, Hufflepuff's cup, Ravenclaw's diadem and Nagini.

The Prophecy

Dumbledore tells Harry about the prophecy and what it means - that neither Harry nor Voldemort can live while the other survives.

The
Diary

The
Locket

The
Ring

Nagini

THE CAVE

Dumbledore and Harry travel to the cave to try and find one of the Horcruxes - Slytherin's locket.

ALBUS
DUMBLEDORE